CONTENTS

WHY SMARTPHONES?

You see it everywhere. Whether eating in a restaurant, walking down a busy sidewalk, sitting at a sporting event, or even driving a car (although the latter is a huge no-no), people tend to have their eyes and fingertips focused on an object cradled in the palm of their hand—their ever-present smartphone.

More than three-quarters of American adults say they own a smartphone, according to the Pew Research Center. Among those between the ages of 50 and 64, the number is 74 percent—only a fraction below the national average. Worldwide, smartphone usage is measured in

If one piece of technology has come close to near ubiquity in the past two decades, it's the smartphone. With early widespread adoption of the technology in Japan, this technology spread into American markets with early iterations like the BlackBerry and Sidekick.

The ways to use a smartphone are as limitless as the internet. Some of the more popular uses include navigation, shopping (either online shopping or looking up product details right while you're in the store), emailing, shooting photos or video, social media, and of course texting.

billions as more and more people forego the computer in order to access the internet on the go.

In fact, for the sake of a definition, a smartphone is simply a mobile phone that functions much like a computer. It offers internet access, has a touchscreen interface, and uses an operating system that runs applications (apps). The most popular types are the iPhone, which turned 10 years old in 2017, and the Android. We will discuss each of these in greater detail.

If you have not yet ventured into the world of smartphones, there are many reasons to consider doing so. And making phone calls is only one of them!

Smartphones truly put the world of computing at your fingertips. They go where you go. Carrying a computer or laptop around can be cumbersome. With a smartphone, you retain much the functionality of a computer in a device that's convenient to carry along.

The top operating systems for smart phones are Apple's iOS for the iPhone and Google's Android which operates on a number of manufacturers' phones including Samsung.

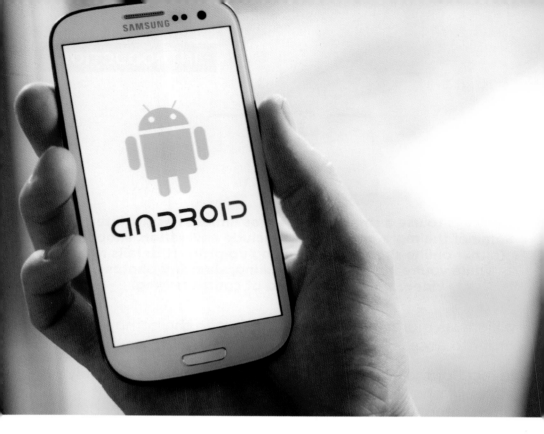

INTRO TO ANDROID

The smartphone landscape is divided into two distinct hemispheres—Android and iPhone. Android is a Google system, while the iPhone is Apple's baby. Which one to choose is entirely a matter of personal preference. Both will equip you with everything you need from your smartphone.

Android is the name of the operating system that Google introduced in 2007. Don't be concerned if you know nothing about operating systems! You don't need to know a thing. Because the Android system can be run on many different smartphone devices, going the Android route allows you to choose your actual phone from several different phone makers—Samsung, Motorola, LG, etc.

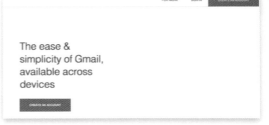

Creating a Google account is free and easy to get started, so it's definitely recommended for Android users.

If you need to create a Google account, go to Gmail.com and then simply click the link that reads *Create an Account*.

The ease & simplicity of Gmail, available across devices

GOOGLE ACCOUNTS AND ANDROID USAGE

Because Android is a Google system, it's best to have a Google account if you will be going the Android route. You can set one up either on your new smartphone or on your computer. And if you use Gmail as your email provider, great news! You already have a Google account.

Having a Google account is not a requirement for using an Android device. However, Google offers a wide variety of services and apps that will enhance your Android experience, and accessing these services *will* require a Google account.

With a Google account you will have access to all of Google's handy apps like Google Maps, Calendar, Chat, Drive, Docs, YouTube, and many more.

USING ANDROID

For first-time smartphone users, it's a great idea to purchase your new device from a cellular service store like Verizon or AT&T. There you will find knowledgeable people who can help you set up your phone and get started with some of the basics.

SETTING UP MOBILE SERVICE

When you first turn on the device, you will be asked to choose a language. That way the rest of the set-up process will need no translation! You will also be asked to insert the SIM card. This tiny card identifies you as the owner of the phone and contains information that allows you to use the features your new smartphone offers. If and when you switch to a new device at some point, the SIM card will make it easier to do so without losing any key information.

One of the first things you will need to do is sign up for cellular service. This will allow you to use the smartphone as—of all things—a phone! You will want to choose a plan that also gives you a certain amount of data usage. Using the internet or apps from your smartphone will incur data usage unless you are hooked up to a Wi-Fi network. That's why connecting to an available Wi-Fi signal is always a smart idea.

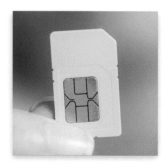

A SIM (subscriber identification module) card is an integrated circuit that is used to verify and authenticate the subscriber identity of mobile network users. It can also be helpful in that it stores your contacts and SMS text messages, making it easier to transfer that information from one phone to another.

ACCESSING WI-FI

Swipe down from the top of your screen to access both your Notification Tray and your Quick Setting toggle screen. Select the *Wi-Fi* button to enable network access.

After you have turned on your Wi-Fi, a screen will pop up identifying the local networks around you. Select the surrounding network you would like to join. Your home Wi-Fi network likely has a security code that you will be prompted to enter. Once connected to Wi-Fi, you won't incur data charges from your mobile service provider when using it.

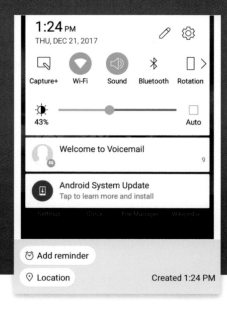

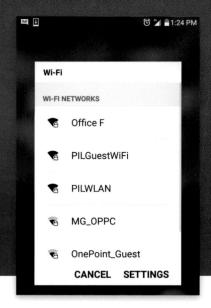

COMPLETING ANDROID SETUP

The set-up process can vary slightly from one type of phone to another, but in general there are a few steps required before you can truly start exploring the many features of your new smartphone.

One of them is signing into your Google account. As discussed, this is optional with Android, but it's highly recommended so you can take advantage of the many services Google offers for Android devices.

When you sign in using your Gmail address and password, you will be asked whether you want to "opt in" to several different services. These are optional, but the one you want to make sure you check *Yes* for is to "automatically back up device data." This way if anything ever happens to your smartphone, Google will have a backup copy of any important information you have stored on your phone.

You will also be asked if you'd like to add another email account to your device. If you have an email address other than the Gmail address used to set up the phone (a different work email address, for example), this is the place to add it. You will need to know both the address and password, of course. You can also skip this step for now and add another email account later.

Two of the final steps in setting up your device will be deciding whether to require a Lock Screen password for security reasons (recommended) and choosing what type of notifications to receive.

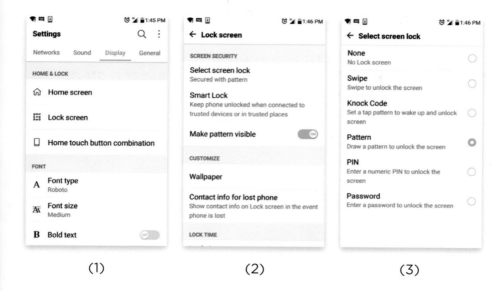

(1)　　　　　　　(2)　　　　　　　(3)

SECURITY

There are a number of ways you can secure your phone. To choose what is best for you, open *Settings* (1) and find the *Security* or *Lock Screen* section (2), and then choose which security method is best for you and easiest to remember (3).

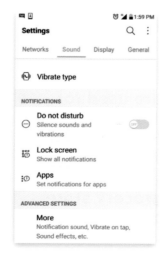

NOTIFICATIONS

To customize your notification settings, open *Settings* and scroll down to find the *Notifications* section. From there you can select which apps you receive notifications from, and what types of notifications you will be given while your phone is locked.

TEXTING ON ANDROID

Text messages, for those new to cell phone use, are quick messages you can send to others on their cell phones. You cannot send text messages to "land lines"—those home phones that don't use cellular technology—but only from one mobile phone to another.

Generally speaking, text messages are used for quick communications that don't require voice-to-voice conversation or the longer email format. If the situation calls for longer-form writing (a detailed recipe, for example), email is probably a better option. If someone is at the grocery store and you need to remind them to pick up butter, however, text messaging is ideal!

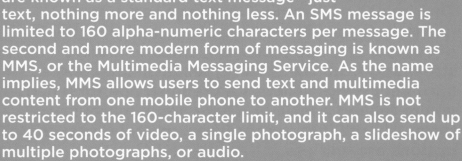

(1)   (2)

SENDING TEXTS

Sending a text message is easy. Simply click on the *Messages* app on your Android phone and you will be taken to the main messaging menu. From there, you will see a history of the conversations you've had. Create a new message, and you will then be asked for a cell phone number or a name (1). Choosing a name from your address book is the recommended option, so you don't have to remember everyone's cell phone number. As you build up new numbers and contacts, it's a great idea to add them to your address book for this purpose.

Once the recipient is chosen (and you can choose more than one), tap in the body field and start typing your message (2). Once you have typed your message, tap the SEND icon and your message will be on its way.

MMS VS. SMS

There are two major formats of text messages that allow you to send different types of media. The first and older form of messaging is SMS, or the Short Message Service. SMS messages are known as a standard text message—just text, nothing more and nothing less. An SMS message is limited to 160 alpha-numeric characters per message. The second and more modern form of messaging is known as MMS, or the Multimedia Messaging Service. As the name implies, MMS allows users to send text and multimedia content from one mobile phone to another. MMS is not restricted to the 160-character limit, and it can also send up to 40 seconds of video, a single photograph, a slideshow of multiple photographs, or audio.

EMOJIS ON ANDROID

"Keeping up with the cool kids" is one of the joys of text messaging. In addition to learning any number of abbreviations like OMG (oh my gosh) and LOL (laughing out loud)—fast becoming a part of everyday speech—there are those popular little smiley faces to incorporate.

Actually, there is far more than little smiley faces to be incorporated into your texting vocabulary. They're called "emojis," and they come in all forms, it seems. The smiley face speaks for itself, of course. The one with a big smile and tears streaming from the eyes represents "laughing so hard I'm crying." There's a greenish one for when you're feeling a little ill. There are numerous sad faces, angry faces, goofy faces, animal faces...the options are endless.

ENABLING YOUR PHONE TO RECEIVE EMOJIS

If you have an older Android device, you may need to check to see if your phone can process emojis. Some cannot. From your device, go to Google and do a search for "emoji." If you see a smattering of little faces in the search results, you're in business! If you see strange-looking boxes or rectangles, your phone may not be equipped for emojis.

Even if your device can handle them, it might not be set up to do so by default. You can enable this functionality by going to *Settings*, finding a section for language or input method, and then making sure you are using your phone's default setting.

If your default keyboard does not include emojis, you can always download a keyboard that does. Google Keyboard, which is an app you can download, is one of the most popular. More on app downloading in the pages to come!

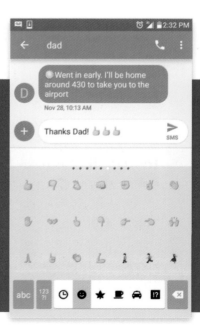

USING EMOJIS

To use emojis while texting, touch the **EMOJI** icon and you be shown a variety of graphics you can use to in your text. There are icons for hand gestures, emotional states, food, activities, and all sorts of objects that you can use for shorthand communication.

15

EMAILING ON ANDROID

Accessing your email is one of the many benefits of owning a smartphone. No need to sit at home and wait for that important correspondence.

ADDING EMAIL ACCOUNTS

If you have another email account you'd like to use instead of (or in addition to) Gmail, you can add it by going to *Settings* on your phone and scrolling to *Accounts*. Tap on *Add Account*. You will then be prompted to type in the email address and your password, and tap *Next*. Depending on the type of account, you may need to add a domain

Because you set up your device with a Google account, there will be a *Gmail* button under the Google app folder along with the icons for the various Google supported apps you have on your phone. Simply tap the icon and you will be given access to your Gmail account wherever you are.

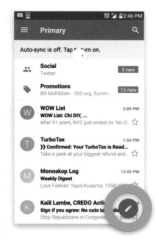

The red, circular button with the PENCIL icon will create a new email composition for you.

name, username, and server name—particularly if this is a work email account. If you don't have all that information for a work account, an IT professional at your workplace should be able to help.

COMPOSING EMAILS

Your own email address should appear in the *From* field. In the *To* field, simply begin typing the name or email address of your intended recipient. As with text messaging, you can send an email to multiple recipients at once if you choose.

The large field below the *Subject* field is the *Body* field, where you type your message. You can also "attach" files, such as photos or documents you have on your smartphone, to an email by clicking on the **PAPER CLIP** icon at the top of your screen. You will then be prompted to select the item you'd like to attach from where it is stored on your device (your photo gallery, for example). Once you have finished your message, hit the **SEND** icon at the top-right corner and it will be on its way!

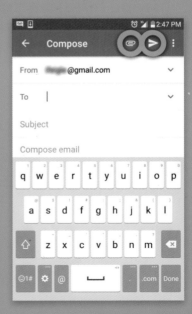

APPS ON ANDROID

The world is, literally, at your fingertips with a smartphone. One of the advantages of Android is the sheer number of applications—or apps—you can download and run. There are millions of them.

To see which ones are on your phone already, swipe left from your Home Screen to see what apps occupy your auxiliary screens. Chances are you will recognize which one to choose to access email from the previous pages. However, the breadth of your options is truly up to you.

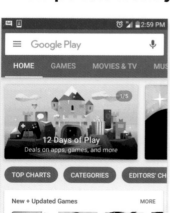

You'll find much more than apps in Google Play. It is the digital media distribution center for the Android operating system, providing users a place to buy magazines, books, music, movies, games, and television programs.

FINDING APPS FOR YOUR ANDROID

The best way to explore and enjoy apps on your Android device is to tap on the *Google Play* button, or the *Play Store*. This is your gateway to everything you might want to do on your new Android smartphone.

Some of the most popular apps will likely appear at the top of the screen. These may include social media apps like Facebook and Instagram, or movie viewing services like Netflix. The popular ones will change, of course, as new apps are developed and adopted.

The price of each app will appear under its name and icon. Many of the best ones are free. If you're not sure what the app does or how it might help you, just click on the logo for more details. You will also see a user rating that summarizes how much others have enjoyed the app.

DOWNLOADING APPS

Simply select the app you would like to download and press *Install* to save the app to your smartphone. If there is a cost, you will be prompted to pay before downloading. Once the app is on your phone, you will see its icon appear on your homescreen. You can now run the app on your phone. (Keep in mind that, when using the app for the first time, you may be required to register using your email address.)

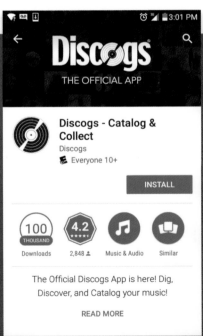

INTRO TO iPHONE

The iPhone, the pride of Apple Inc., celebrated its 10th anniversary in 2017 with the iPhone X. Apple skipped nine in its numbering sequence in honor of the milestone.

iPhone users tend to be extremely passionate about the product. Despite its recognizable design and loyal following, the main difference between the iPhone and Android is the operating system.

iPhone's operating system is called iOS. Unlike Android, iOS was made exclusively for Apple. So, if it's iOS you choose for your smartphone purchase, you're in the market for an iPhone.

Again, it's a matter of preference. Several sources are constantly comparing iPhone and Android, but there's not necessarily a winner or loser. Android certainly

This iPhone 8 has Touch ID, which allows its users to unlock their phones by scanning their fingerprints. But today, the iPhone X has increased its security measures with a facial recognition feature called Face ID.

offers more choices when it comes to the phone itself. And there have traditionally been more apps available for Android than for iPhone. iPhone loyalists, however, can point to several ease-of-use advantages—in addition to the knowledge that when the operating system is updated (that is, improved upon in some way), iPhone users generally have an easier time keeping up with the updates due to the consistency of the phones. None of that is of huge importance as you purchase your first smartphone and begin exploring. Welcome to that world!

PICKING A PLAN

A cell phone carrier is a great place to start when trying to decide whether or not you want to go the Android or iOS route. Visit a Verizon, AT&T or other

carrier's store and let them help you decide which plan and which phone fits your needs and your budget. Apple has long prided itself on a unique, streamlined, and easy-to-follow user-experience model for its computers and phones, while Android is very convenient in that it can be used across multiple manufacturers. Getting to know each operating system and their capabilities and disadvantages can help you decide which is best for you.

SETTING UP YOUR iPHONE

You will be greeted by the word *Hello* in several languages when you turn on an iPhone for the first time. Choosing your language, and your home country, is the first order of business. As with most things Apple, it's an easy, one-click process.

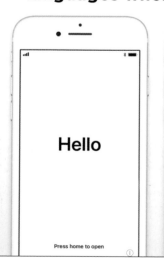

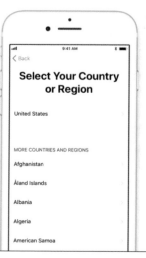

QUICK START VS. MANUAL

There's a Quick Start set-up process for those already using iOS on another device. In the case of a first-time user, you should choose the Manual set-up process. Don't be intimidated. Manual does not mean more "complicated."

The first step will be choosing a wireless network, which you will be prompted to do. If you are in a mobile carrier store, a representative will likely be able to help you do this (and will likely walk you through the set-up process). If you're at home, connect to your existing wireless network. This will allow you to follow the remaining steps in setting up your iPhone.

TOUCH ID AND SECURITY

Some of the newer iPhones, models 6S through 8 Plus, have a feature called Touch ID, where you can press the main **HOME** button and unlock your phone

using your fingerprint. If your phone has this feature, the set-up process will show you how to configure it. Whether or not your phone has Touch ID, you will also choose a numerical password that will allow you to lock your phone to prevent unwanted use from someone other than you.

WELCOME TO iTUNES

Just as a Google account powers the best features and services of Android, joining iTunes is your entry to the world of iOS. You can join iTunes on your smartphone or through the iTunes app on your computer.

APPLE ID

Once you have set up an Apple ID and password on iTunes, you can enter it during the iPhone set-up process and your phone will automatically be linked to your iTunes account. Why is this important?

Well, just as a Google account can back up your important information from Android and allow you to access a wealth of apps that make your phone

Create Your Apple ID

One Apple ID is all you need to access all Apple services.
Already have an Apple ID? Find it here ›

first name   last name

United States

birthday

name@example.com
This will be your new Apple ID

password

confirm password

Security Question 1

answer

Security Question 2

answer

Security Question 3

answer

These questions will be used to verify your identity and recover your
password if you ever forget it.

☑ Announcements
Get announcements, recommendations, and updates about Apple products,
services, software updates, and more.

☑ Apple Music, New Apps and More
Get recommendations, the latest releases, special offers, and exclusive
content for music, apps, movies, TV, books, podcasts and more.

☑ Apple News Updates
Get the best stories and recommendations from Apple News delivered
directly to your inbox.

You will need an email address and a solid password that you will remember in order to create your Apple ID.

experience the best it can be, iTunes is your safety net and key to maximizing all that iOS offers.

There may also be a few privacy questions toward the end of the set-up process. You could be asked how much information about your phone usage you would be willing to share with developers in the interest of improving the iOS software or the iPhone itself. There are no right or wrong answers here—just a matter of your own comfort level. Finally, you should see two magic words: *Get Started*. Time to explore!

WHAT IS SIRI?

A few other items of note in the set-up process. You may be asked to speak a few phrases into your phone. That's to set up a voice control called "Siri." The voice of Siri can answer questions for you,

Siri

Use your voice to send messages, set reminders, search for information, and more.

help you find things and even suggest things to do if you decide to use the voice activation offered by iPhone. Once you get going on your phone, try asking Siri a question by holding down the main **HOME** button until your phone asks, "What can I help you with?"

TEXT AND EMAIL ON iPHONE

Sending and receiving text messages on an iPhone works much like it does on an Android, although you might note a subtle difference in the background color of the messages. When sending a message from one iPhone to another, the text will send as an iMessage and will have a blue background. When sending to an Android phone, the message will go through as a text message and the background will be green.

Either way, your message arrives as typed. When iMessaging, the user can typically see a series of dots that indicate that the other person is typing.

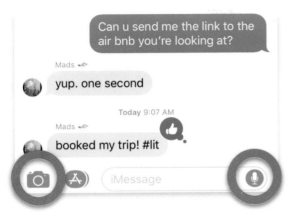

By tapping the
MICROPHONE icon on
the bottom-right of your
screen, you can dictate
messages to your phone
as opposed to typing
them out.

iMESSAGE FEATURES

There are also a few unique features when texting on
an iPhone. By tapping one of the texts, you will have
options to add THUMBS UP or THUMBS DOWN emojis to a
comment, or even laugh at it. These emojis will be added
to the text. In addition, clicking the CAMERA icon next to
the *iMessage* field allows you to snap a quick photo to
insert into your message.

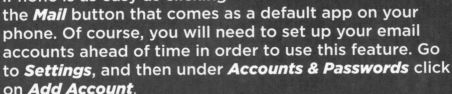

ACCESSING EMAIL

Accessing your email on the
iPhone is as easy as clicking
the *Mail* button that comes as a default app on your
phone. Of course, you will need to set up your email
accounts ahead of time in order to use this feature. Go
to *Settings*, and then under *Accounts & Passwords* click
on *Add Account*.

You can set up accounts from any email provider,
including Google (Gmail). No Android phone required!

iPHONE APPS

Apps for the iPhone are purchased (or downloaded free of charge) through iTunes. There are a couple of ways to do this.

From your iPhone, click on the *App Store* app. There will be featured apps showcased at the top of the page, but you can also sort by using the navigation at the bottom. You can search for an app you have heard about and want to download, or you can browse among popular apps. As with Android apps, some are free of charge while others come with a purchase price. Purchases of iPhone apps are handled, again, through iTunes.

SYNCING YOUR iPHONE WITH YOUR COMPUTER

You can also browse for apps on a computer if a larger screen makes shopping easier. Apps that you purchase

on your computer can be added to your phone by plugging your iPhone into your laptop or desktop computer and "syncing" your phone with iTunes. This is also a great way to back up your phone, and to share music purchases between your iPhone and computer.

By using iTunes, you are essentially linking all the Apple products you use with one another. This also goes for products like the Apple Watch, but that's a technology subject for another venue!

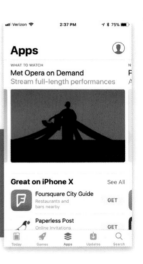

The variety of apps you can download for your iPhone is seemingly limitless. The Met Opera on Demand app is an example of this enormous variety.

Organizing Your Apps

Touch and hold any app on the screen until they all jiggle.

Now you can drag any app to another spot, including the Dock at the bottom of the screen.

Press the Home button to save. Or on an iPhone X, press Done.

Organizing Apps Into Folders

To make a folder, drag an app onto another app.

If you want to rename the folder, tap the name field or ⊗ and then enter the new name.

Now that you have a folder, you can drag apps into it. Folders can have more than one page.

USING YOUR iPHONE'S CAMERA

Taking photos and videos on an iPhone is as easy as it gets. Simply click on the *Camera* button, and your smartphone becomes a combination camera and video camera. You can switch from one to the other by swiping left or right once in camera mode. There are also options to take time-lapse, slow motion, and panoramas.

USING FACETIME

You might have seen people talking into their iPhones while looking at the other person. It's a terrific Apple feature called FaceTime, which allows video calling.

Instead of clicking on the *Mobile* button when you call one of your contacts, you can choose the little